To the men and women of the United States who have given the final full measure in service to our nation. God Bless You, Your Families, and the United States of America!

A special thank you to the United States Army 3rd Infantry Regiment (Old Guard) for the behind-the-scenes access to the Caisson Platoon at Fort Myer, Virginia. Robert and I discovered a team of Soldiers and Horses with tremendous energy, unwavering dedication, and a commitment to their mission in Arlington National Cemetery. Theirs is a life dedicated to an expression of heartfelt gratitude from our nation to those special men and women who have served a cause greater than themselves.

The children loved to visit Grandma and Grandpa at their home in the nation's capital. During the Cherry Blossom Festival they enjoyed walks along the Tidal Basin to the Jefferson Memorial. On the 4th of July they delighted in watching the brilliant fireworks display on the Mall.

In October, the family took pleasure in cheering the runners in the Army 10 Miler and the Marine Corps Marathon as they made their way through the nation's capital to the finish line.

At Christmas, the family loved to see the decorations throughout Washington, DC, especially the National Christmas Tree aglow in front of the White House.

Their favorite place to visit was the stables of The Old Guard's Caisson Platoon on Fort Myer, Virginia. The children loved to pet and feed the horses. It made them very happy when the horses stretched out their long necks into the hallway to greet them.

Grandpa explained the importance of the Caisson Platoon. "These horses are an important part of our nation's history and its military traditions. They have a very special mission in Arlington National Cemetery. The duty of the Soldiers of the Caisson Platoon is to care for the horses, clean their stalls, and prepare the saddles and bridles for the horses. The Soldiers and horses work together to ensure they are ready each and every day to work their very special mission in Arlington National Cemetery."

Grandpa paused for a moment.

"What is the special mission of the horses, Grandpa?" the children asked.

"The horses' special mission in Arlington National Cemetery is to carry the nation's fallen warriors to their final resting place in the cemetery. It's a military tradition and symbol of respect to our fallen warriors and their families who have served the nation with honor, courage, and dignity," Grandpa explained seriously.

During their visits, the children noticed Grandpa always brought a special treat of carrots and a big shiny red apple for one particular horse named Mark. When Grandpa walked toward Mark's stall, the horse waved his head, stomped his hoof, and neighed happily as if to greet Grandpa. The playful actions of Mark always made Grandma and Grandpa giggle with laughter.

Grandma told the children, "Mark the horse reminds Grandpa of his brother, Mark, who passed away long ago. The white wisps of hair on Mark's nose resemble the white patch Grandpa's brother had in his black head of hair." Now the children understood more clearly why Grandpa and Mark got along so well.

In the stables, the children were always intrigued by the Soldiers in their brown shirts, blue jeans, cowboy boots, and stetsons. The children loved to help the Soldiers with their many chores around the stables when they visited. They always helped the Soldiers feed and groom the horses when they visited the stables which made the children feel very special!

The Soldiers had many chores to complete at the stables. They had to clean the stalls of the horses, polish the saddles and bridles, and ensure the horses remained in good health. The Soldiers also ensured the caissons were ready to go each and every day to carry out their special mission in Arlington National Cemetery.

One of the children's favorite activities was watching the stable's farrier trim the hooves of the horses and place new horseshoes on the horses to protect them.

One day, Grandpa, Grandma, and the children arrived at the stables earlier than usual. Mark had never seen Grandpa dressed in his immaculate Army uniform nor Grandma and the children dressed in their Sunday's finest outfits.

"Well, old boy, we have a very special mission to complete today," sighed Grandpa as he gave Mark his bounty of carrots and an apple, and hugged Mark's long neck.

The children knew a dear, old friend of Grandpa's that served many years in the military would be laid to rest in Arlington National Cemetery this very day. Grandpa's friend had led Soldiers in combat and had fought bravely for the freedom of people around the world.

Mark could tell Grandpa was sad today but he knew his team had a mission to complete. The horses and Soldiers of the Caisson Platoon had the distinct honor of carrying Grandpa's friend to his final resting place in Arlington National Cemetery today.

Suddenly, the stables became a flurry of activity as the Soldiers of the Caisson Platoon readied the horses for their very special mission. First, they bathed the horses in a special stall. Then, the Soldiers placed the harnesses and saddles on each horse. Next, the Soldiers rolled out the caissons from the stables and prepared their uniforms. Finally, the Soldiers hitched the team of six horses to the caisson and finished dressing the team.

The team of Soldiers, dressed in their uniforms and riding boots, prepared to mount the horses. The Sergeant inspected each Soldier to ensure every detail on his uniform was perfect.

Grandpa and the children watched on as the Soldiers prepared to mount the horses. "The team of horses and their riders are ready for their mission," Grandpa whispered to the children. "During the Civil War the caisson was used to carry supplies to the Soldiers on the front lines and deliver wounded Soldiers to the hospital for medical care. The caisson team consists of six horses and three riders. The Sergeant of the caisson team rides a separate horse nearer the front to lead the team," Grandpa explained carefully to the children.

The Sergeant commanded, "Riders, prepare to mount!" The Soldiers placed one boot in the stirrup of the saddle. The Sergeant then commanded, "Mount!" In perfect unison, the Soldiers rose to the top of their saddles.

The Sergeant of the caisson team read off the names of the fallen warriors to be honored that day. Today, one name held a special place in Grandpa's heart. His dear friend was to be taken to his final resting place in Arlington National Cemetery. The team of horses and Soldiers of the Caisson Platoon moved out sharply to the Memorial Chapel to meet Grandpa's friend and begin the military procession into the cemetery.

After the memorial ceremony at the chapel, a team of Soldiers carried the casket to the caisson waiting outside. An American flag, a symbol of patriotism, was draped over the casket. Grandpa and the Soldiers stood at attention and saluted smartly as Grandpa's friend was placed on the caisson for transport into Arlington National Cemetery.

"Forward march!" the Sergeant shouted.

Grandpa, Grandma, and the children walked with the family and friends of the fallen warrior in a procession behind the caisson.

As the caisson approached a long hill, the team of horses clip-clopped along the paved roadway of the cemetery. The children noticed a horse being led by a single Soldier. The children asked Grandpa, "Why is that Soldier not riding the horse?"

Grandpa remarked, "The horse is a Caparisoned horse. The rider-less horse is a cap horse which wears a cavalry saddle, a sword, and riding boots that are placed backwards in the stirrups. It is reserved for special occasions when a fallen warrior has served as a Colonel or General Officer in the Army or Marine Corps like my friend. The cap horse is also used during state funerals to honor the President of the United States, who is also the nation's Commander in Chief."

The children thought Grandpa knew everything and everyone since he was always full of wonderful stories and interesting facts to tell them.

When the team of horses came to a stop, a detail of Soldiers removed the casket from the caisson and set it alongside a group of chairs placed near the gravesite. Grandpa marched with the detail as they placed the casket into position. The children and the rest of the procession took their seats along the gravesite. A chaplain led the memorial service as the family and friends paid their final respects to Grandpa's friend.

At the conclusion of the memorial ceremony, a Sergeant commanded a firing party near the gravesite to fire three volleys in unison as a sign of respect and honor for Grandpa's friend. The sounds of the rifle fire echoed throughout the cemetery. Mark and the other horses looked back, awaiting the sound of the bugler that was to come next.

Grandpa watched on as a team of Soldiers carefully folded the American flag atop of the casket into thirteen tight, neat triangles. Grandpa carefully secured the flag from the Sergeant and respectfully transferred the flag to an Army officer who then presented the stars and stripes to his friend's family.

Grandpa could overhear the Army officer as he presented the stars and stripes to his friend's family, saying, "This flag is presented on behalf of a grateful nation and the United States Army as a token of appreciation for your loved one's honorable and faithful service." As the Army officer placed the flag with the family, the family was solemn in their appreciation holding the flag close to their hearts.

Over the hill, a bugler sounded Taps. The notes echoed throughout the cemetery as Mark and the caisson team made their way back to the stables. Grandpa's friend had been laid to rest in Arlington National Cemetery—a final tribute to honor his service to the nation.

With the ceremony and the mission of the Caisson Platoon complete, Grandpa, Grandma, and the children returned to the stables. Grandpa leaned in to hug Mark as the horse hung its head outside his stall. Grandpa said, "Thank you, old boy. You and your team did a great job today!"

Mark swayed his head and stomped his hoof as if to say, "You're welcome, Sir. It was our pleasure."

To Grandpa's delight the rest of the horses in the stable neighed and stomped at the floor in their stalls too. "Well," Grandpa laughed, "that is more than I could say with words."

Grandma and the children tried to hold back their laughter but after hearing Grandpa's comment, they couldn't help it! After such a special day spent with special friends for a very special mission, it was good to laugh.

As night fell on Arlington National Cemetery, Mark and the other horses rested in preparation for tomorrow's special mission.

Mark gazed from his stall upon the stars in the sky. He thought about the solemn occasion today, and Grandpa and his dear friend.

Today the horses and Soldiers of the Caisson Platoon created a special memory for a family to remember their loved one who was honored this very day.

On this day a friend and a warrior was laid to rest with the respect and honors of a grateful nation surrounded by the love and adoration of his family and friends.

Mark neighed with pride about the special mission he and his team had in Arlington National Cemetery!

About the Author

Gregory P. Keeney currently resides in the Washington, DC area with his wife, Kelly, and three children. He has served in the military for over two decades with multiple combat tours in Afghanistan and Iraq and is a veteran of Desert Shield/Desert Storm. Greg has previously published articles for professional journals, newspapers, and has contributed to *The Saturday Evening Post*.

About the Illustrator

Robert Gantt Steele, the illustrator, is a native of North Carolina and lives with his wife, Alice, and two children near San Francisco. His passion for the American experience is evident in the drama and accuracy of his paintings. Robert developed his love of military history at Fort Belvoir, Virginia, where he served his US Army engineer officer basic training. He has painted for the National Park Service, the United States Air Force, for many books and magazines including *Smithsonian*, and for many events and publications commemorating American history.